Royal College
of Physicians

A year in the
Medicinal Garden
of the Royal College
of Physicians

Dr Henry Oakeley

Revised edition

Citation of this book: Oakeley, H. A *year in the Medicinal Garden of the Royal College of Physicians*, revised edition. London: Royal College of Physicians, 2011.

ISBN: 978-1-86016-451-4

Royal College of Physicians
11 St Andrews Place
Regent's Park
London NW1 4LE

www.rcplondon.ac.uk

Registered Charity No 210508

Further copies of this book are available to order from: www.rcplondon.ac.uk

British Library Cataloguing in Publication Data
A catalogue record of this book is available from the British Library

Text and photography by Dr Henry Oakeley
Contents page photography by Jonathan Perugia

Acknowledgement: Dr Anthony Dayan FRCP, medical text reviewer
Designed by James Partridge, Publications Department, Royal College of Physicians
Printed in Great Britain by Charlesworth Press, Wakefield, West Yorkshire.

A year in the Medicinal Garden
of the Royal College of Physicians

Cover image: Knautia macedonica with bee

Among the plants used as medicines, at some time in the past millennia up to the present day, we have plants named after doctors. This plant commemorates Christof Knaut (1638–94), a German doctor and botanist, author of *Enumeratio Plantarum circa Halam Saxonum … Sponte Provenientium* (1687), brother of the botanist Christian Knaut (1654–1716), author of *Compendium Botanicum sive Methodus plantarum genuina* (1716), a pre-Linnean classification of flowering plants.

Contents

Contents

Sources

In the belief that a reference to a stated fact is better than an apocryphal, unattributable story, herewith the main sources of information on the plants discussed in this little book.

> Austin, D.F. *Florida ethnobotany*. Boca Raton, Fla/London: CRC, 2004.
> Barnes, J, Anderson, LA, Phillipson, J.D. *Herbal medicines*, 3rd edn. London: Pharmaceutical Press, 2007.
> Beck, LY. *Pedanius Dioscorides of Anazarbus. De materia medica*. Hildesheim, New York: Olms-Weidmann, 2005. An English translation of the works of Dioscorides.
> Culpeper, N. *A Physicall Directory* (1649); *The English Physitian* (1652); *Pharmacopoeia londinensis; or the London dispensatory* (1653).
> Foster, S, Duke, JA. *A field guide to medicinal plants: eastern and central North America*. Boston, Mass: Houghton Mifflin, 1990.
> Fuchs, Leonhart. *De Historia Stirpium commentarii insignes* (1542 and 1551).
> Johnson, T. *The herball or General Historie of Plants* (1633). The revised edition (with additions) of John Gerard's *Herball or General Historie of Plants* (1597), which was an English translation of *Stirpium Historiae Pemptades Sex* (1583), which was the Latin version of Dodoens' herbal, the *Cruydeboeck* (1554), much of which is copied from Fuchs, who relies heavily on Dioscorides.
> Lewis, WH, Elvin-Lewis, MPF. *Medical botany*. New Jersey: Wiley, 2003.
> Lindley, J. *Flora Medica* (1838).
> L'Obel (Lobel), Matthias de. *Plantarum seu Stirpium Historia* (1576).
> Lyte, Henry. *Nieuwe Herball or Historie of Plantes* (1578). An English translation of L'Écluse's French translation of Dodoens' herbal, the *Cruydeboeck* (1554).
> Mabberley, D.J. *The plant-book: a portable dictionary of the vascular plants*, 2nd edn. Cambridge: Cambridge University Press, 2002.
> Millspaugh, CE. *American medical plants*. New York/London: Dover Publications/Constable, 1974.
> Moerman, DE. *North American ethnobotany*. Portland, Or: Timber Press, 2009.
> Parkinson, John. *Paradisi in Sole* (1629).
> Porta, GB. *Phytognomonica* (1588). This explains the Doctrine of Signatures.
> Ruellio, Joanne. *Pedanii Dioscoridis Anzarabei de Medicinali Materia Libri sex* (1543). A Latin translation and commentary on the works of Dioscorides.
> Turner, William. *A New Herball* (1551). Edited by G Chapman and M Tweddle. Mid Northumberland Arts Group and Carcanet Press, 1989.
> Van Wyk, B-E et al. *Medicinal plants of South Africa*. Pretoria: Briza, 1997.
> Woodville, William. *Medical botany* (in four volumes, 1790–94).

Famous names in early medical botany

Hippocrates 460–370 BC
Aristotle 384–322 BC
Theophrastus 371–287 BC
Pliny (the Elder) 23–79
Pedanius Dioscorides 40–90
Galen 129–200(+)
Leonhart Fuchs 1501–66
Matthiolus (Pietro Andrea Gregorio Mattioli) 1501–77

Rembert Dodoens 1517–85
Henry Lyte 1529–1607
Giovanni Battista della Porta 1535–1615
Matthias de L'Obel (Lobel) 1538–1616
John Gerard 1545–1612
John Parkinson 1567–1650
Nicholas Culpeper 1616–1654
Carl Linnaeus 1707–78
John Lindley 1795–1865

Preface

The Medicinal Garden of the Royal College of Physicians contains 1,278 different species that are used, or have been used, in medicine during the past two millennia, and ones that commemorate physicians. Many are of no medicinal use, but like the ancient books in the RCP library, record the beliefs and practices of past ages and cultures. This is not a garden set out to be merely decorative; its fascination lies in its plants, in their uses and their dangers, the history and the folklore surrounding them, and even in their names and the influence they have had on the English language.

In this book are set out some of the plants, as they flower week by week through the year, with a commentary on their uses, and notes on the confusion of ancient names. There were many early herbals that were copied in manuscript over the centuries until the advent of printing in the 15th century and none was more influential than the *Materia Medica* of Pedanius Dioscorides of Anazarbus (40–90 AD). I have used the English translation by Lily Beck, but the descriptions are brief and there are no illustrations. I have therefore, arbitrarily, selected the Latin edition of *Materia Medica* by Joanne Ruellio (1543), with its illustrations, as an aid to identifying Dioscorides' plants. Leonhart Fuchs' groundbreaking herbal, *De Historia Stirpium* (1542), gives further help with its excellent woodcuts and has some of the earliest illustrations and commentaries on the new plants from the Americas. Mathias de Lobel's (1576) *Plantarum seu Stirpium Historia* is another wonderful source.

The books that were of the greatest help were, naturally, in English, although both are second generation translations of Rembert Dodoens' *Cruydeboeck* (1554). They are Henry Lyte's *Nievve Herball or Historie of Plantes* (1578) and Gerard's herbal of 1597 – using the corrected second edition herbal of 1597 – using the corrected second edition by Thomas Johnson – *The Herball or General Historie of Plants* (1633). Turner's *A New Herball*

(1551) has fascinating discussions but few plants. I enjoy the style of Nicholas Culpeper in *A Physicall Directory* (1649), *The English Physitian* (1652) and the *Pharmacopoeia Londinensis or the London dispensatory* (1653), but he often plagiarises Lyte so I have only quoted him occasionally.

This book is not an exhaustive treatise on the medicinal qualities, mythological or real, of these plants but I have added comments from William Woodville's *Medical botany* (1790–94), which owes an inordinate amount to the work of Peter Bergius's *Materia Medica* (2nd edition, 1782), and from the prolific Dr John Lindley's *Flora Medica* (1838) to obtain a perspective on the disappearance of the beliefs of the early herbalists into the 19th century.

For the uses of plants with North American origins I have relied on Austin, Foster, Moerman and Millspaugh who collected them from the oral traditions and historical records of the Native Americans. Lastly, I have indicated current medicinal usage from modern scientific authorities. On the internet, sources such as Wikipedia, Plants for a Future, the Kew Monocot List, the International Plant Name Index and others have pointed me in directions of use, information and accuracy.

This is a book for interest and none of the plants should be eaten, drunk or smoked, except a few such as *Camellia sinensis* which makes a perfectly legal cup of tea. If stories about the history of plants in the progress of medicine, as exemplified by this selection of plants from our Medicinal Garden, whet your appetite for more, then visit the garden pages at www.rcplondon.ac.uk/museum-garden/garden.

Dr Henry Oakeley
Garden Fellow

January

1

2

3

4

5

6

7

Primula veris – cowslip: a confusion of names

It is not usual for the cowslip to be in flower in January, but in some years it seems to be in flower almost every month in the Medicinal Garden. It is still abundant in parts of Britain, but such is the urbanisation of our population that few people who visit the garden even know the name. In the 16th century the confusion concerning its identity was in its multiple names. Cowslips were known as *Artheticae, Arthriticae, Verbasculum odoratum, Verbascum, Herba paralysis,* lychnitis and thryallis/thryallida, St Peter's herb, primroses and little mulleins – and as a pot herb (for eating). They were thought by some to be the *Alisma* or the *Phlomides* of Dioscorides. Johnson regarded them as good for arthritis, paralysis, renal stones, tonsillitis (as a gargle) and all chest complaints. Lindley notes that the flowers are sedative and make a pleasant soporific wine. Cowslips contain active saponins, which can cause dermatitis. It is not used in medicine today; nor is it licensed in the UK as a traditional herbal remedy.

January

8 _____

9 _____

10 _____

11 _____

12 _____

13 _____

14 _____

Eranthis hyemalis – winter aconite: a confusion of plants

The name 'aconite' was given to three different groups of plants by the 16th-century herbalists. *Eranthis hyemalis*, the February flowering, winter aconite, was known as *Aconitum hyemale*, winter woolfes-bane, by Johnson. Lyte called it *Lycoctonus luteum minus* – little yellow wolfsbane. The leaves resemble those of the true wolfbane or monkshood – *Aconitum lycoctonum* and *Aconitum napellus* – but the golden daisy-like flowers are quite different and it is not related in any way. *Doronicum pardalianches*, leopard's bane, which also has golden, daisy-like flowers, was classified as an *Aconitum* and its properties similarly confused. All were regarded as being as poisonous as the true *Aconitum* and used for poisoning wolves and dogs. The roots of *Aconitum napellus* were said to resemble a scorpion, so Ruellio, by inference, stated that they were especially poisonous to scorpions.

January

15

16

17

18

19

20

21

Physalis alkekengi – Chinese lanterns: food, poison and future medicines

A European native, we call it Chinese lanterns or winter cherry. Dioscorides knew that the plant was not edible but recommended the fruit as a diuretic and good for clearing jaundice. Fuchs called it *Helicacabum peregrinum*, attributing sedative properties to the root, and thought the fruit was diuretic. Lyte listed it as red nightshade and *Vesicaria peregrinum*, placing it, as did all the herbalists, with other Solanaceae such as deadly nightshade, mandrake, henbane and tomatoes. The beautiful, edible, autumnal, orange fruits in the skeletal remnants of their covering calyces persist into the new year. They are served in exotic fruit salads and with meat dishes – sweet and delicious – but unripe they (like the rest of the plant) are poisonous, containing the toxic alkaloid solanine. Its potential for medicine is enormous: it contains physalins that may be developed into new drugs against leukaemias and lung cancer; cytostigmines that may treat congenital lipid storage disorders such as Gaucher's syndrome; and extracts of the plant are claimed to kill parasitic trypanosomes and the bacterium which causes gonorrhoea.

A year in the Medicinal Garden of the Royal College of Physicians 5

January

22

23

24

25

26

27

28

Ranunculus ficaria – lesser celandine, pilewort and figwort: for piles

Carrying the roots, or applying a paste made from them, alleviated haemorrhoids/piles, according to Lyte. An early English name for a haemorrhoid was a 'fig' and 'ficaria' means 'pertaining to piles'. Celandine is a corruption of the Greek word 'chelidonion', meaning a swallow. It was said to flower when the swallows appeared and to wither away when they left, according to Lyte. However, Dioscorides attributes this phenomenon to our greater celandine, *Chelidonium majus*, which starts later and continues in flower until the autumn. Of course, in southern Italy the proverb is 'One swallow does not make a spring', as opposed to the English 'One swallow does not make a summer', and they appear earlier and leave even later in the land of Dioscorides. Plants in the buttercup family, Ranunculaceae, tend to be poisonous and are among the few plants that thrive in alpine meadows when cows are present. The cows avoid them but eat almost all the other wild flowers.

January

29

30

31

Notes

Olea europaea – the olive: hope and friendship

Dioscorides regarded the olive as a panacea, curing all manner of cutaneous afflictions from shingles to sores, eye problems to bleeding, and for cleaning gums. However, the sap he regarded as a deadly poison, an abortifacient, but good for curing leprosy if applied topically. Other 16th-century herbalists repeat Dioscorides, but by Lindley's time the bark had also acquired a reputation as a quinine substitute and was used for fevers. The medicinal virtues now reside only in the oil, which is low in monounsaturated fat. Ingestion of 23 g a day instead of saturated fats may reduce the risk of coronary heart disease. It is also used to soften ear wax. Olive fruit takes much longer to ripen in northern latitudes, which is why we see it in midwinter still on our tree. The RCP's tree was presented as a token of friendship by the Society of Apothecaries.

February

1 _____

2 _____

3 _____

4 _____

5 _____

6 _____

7 _____

Galanthus nivalis – the snowdrop: to help us remember

The chemical galantamine is sourced principally from the Caucasian snowdrop, *Galanthus woronowii*, but is present in our 'English' snowdrop and related species. It is a competitive, reversible, acetylcholinesterase inhibitor that increases brain acetylcholine, a chemical of great importance in cerebral function. As such it has been recommended for ameliorating the symptoms of mild to moderate Alzheimer's disease, but not for mild cognitive impairment due to increased mortality in US clinical trials.

Some authors have regarded Homer's 'moly' (used by Circe to poison Odysseus's men) as being this plant, but 16th-century herbalists (and Linnaeus) were clear that 'moly' was an *Allium*, a member of the onion family. Johnson calls it the bulbous violet, *Viola theophrasti, Leucoium* or snowdrop, and says there is no mention of it by ancient writers and that it has no medicinal use. Fuchs calls it *Leucoium theophrasti*, known to Pliny, and *Viola alba*, and concurs that it is of no use. The woodcuts in these herbals are immensely useful in identifying *G. nivalis* despite its alternative names.

February

8

9

10

11

12

13

14

Hepatica nobilis – liverwort: not good for the liver

Hepatica is the Greek word for the liver, and the three-lobed leaf of this little herbaceous plant with its bright blue flowers indicated, according to the Doctrine of Signatures, that it should be of value for the treatment of liver diseases as the liver has three lobes. Johnson calls it noble liverwort, or golden trefoile, *Hepatica trifolium* and *herbe trinite*, to be used for 'weakness of the liver'. Otherwise, it is not found in 16th- to 19th-century herbals or medical botany texts. Moerman reports that the Cherokee and Chippewa of North America used it for liver disorders and as a poultice for bruises, but much of their medical practice developed after the introduction of European ideas. Two hundred metric tons of dried *Hepatica* leaves were harvested in 1883 in Canada for liver tonics (immensely popular for treating 'liverishness', whatever that might be) which caused cases of jaundice. Perhaps the three-lobed leaf was a warning that it should not be used for the liver, but it is a member of the buttercup family, Ranunculaceae, so we should know it is toxic.

February

15

16

17

18

19

20

21

Narcissus pseudonarcissus – wild daffodil: admire but do not eat

Our English wild daffodil had many names in the past, including Lent lily, bastard narcissus, yellow crowbels, narcissus lute and *Pseudonarcissus*. It is found throughout Western Europe. All parts of the plant are poisonous, especially the bulbs, although Lyte thought that the root boiled in water with a little anise or fennel seed and ginger cured coughs. Dangerously, online herbals still recommend it for bronchitis in children. In the long evolution of mankind by natural selection, those of our ancestors who had delicate stomachs vomited before a poison was digested and absorbed into the body. Those who could 'eat anything' died out. Dioscorides, writing on *Narcissus poeticus*, wrote that the bulbs made one vomit if eaten (a clear sign that they are poisonous), but they were good for healing wounds and ulcers if plastered on. Johnson, adding to Dodoens' text, writes that the 'distilled water of daffodils' will cure someone of a stroke ('palsy') if the patient is bathed with it and has it rubbed on, beside a fire. As a measure of global warming, the daffodil now flowers two months earlier than it did a century ago.

February

22

23

24

25

26

27

28

Pulmonaria officinalis – lungwort: a plethora of names and no uses

The hairy leaves covered with white spots resemble the cut surface of a lung, hence the name and its early usage for pulmonary disorders. It was used as a pot-herb (vegetable) and Johnson reports it as good against infirmities and ulcers of the lungs, calling it *Pulmonaria foliis Echii* or 'buglosse cowslip'. A hot poultice would be made from the leaves and applied to the chest. Lyte said it was of no use in medicine, but was eaten as a salad. Herbalists muddled it up with comfrey, *Symphytum officinale*, which has similar flowers. Lyte calls it *Pulmonaria*, lungwort, *Symphitum sylvestre* or wild comfrey, sage of Jerusalem, cowslip of Jerusalem and our ladies milkeworte ('because the leaves be full of white spottes as though they were sprinkled with milke'). Woodville writes that it has no medicinal effect, but Linnaeus (1753) kept its medicinal, historical name when he gave it the name which we still use today.

February

29

Notes

Petasites hybridus – butterbur: a curious remedy for a curious disorder

Butterbur or bog rhubarb grows in Europe and north-west Asia. Dioscorides recommended the ground-up leaves, applied as a poultice, as a topical treatment for 'malignant and cancerous ulcers'. Lyte regarded it as an exceptional medicine against plague as it caused sweating, and that it was also good for treating intestinal worms and for the 'suffocation and strangling of the mother'. In this latter curious phrase 'mother' means 'womb', and refers to mental disorders in women, which were thought to be due to disorders of the womb, in particular the then current concept that the womb wandered about the body and had to be brought back to its correct position by aromatic pessaries. We still use the word 'hysterical' for types of mental illness, not realising that it too stems from the curious idea that it was similarly caused, for the word comes from 'husterikos', the Greek for the womb.

Modern herbalists recommend *Petasites* for a wide range of therapies, but caution that it contains potentially toxic alkaloids so internal use is not advised.

March

1 _____

2 _____

3 _____

4 _____

5 _____

6 _____

7 _____

Caulophyllum thalictroides – blue cohosh: in bringing life it took it away

Blue cohosh, also known as squaw root and papoose root, is a North American woodland plant with fleshy blue, seed-containing berries. Millspaugh reports that it was used by Native Americans to promote labour. Pregnant women took it for a month or two before childbirth. Seventy years ago it was in the *British Pharmacopoeia*, when extracts from the roots and rhizomes were used as a diuretic. It causes contraction of smooth and voluntary muscle, and may cause chorea-like involuntary movements. It can cause serious myocardial toxicity (heart failure) and strokes in newborn babies whose mothers have taken blue cohosh, as it contains cardiotoxic alkaloids and vasoconstrictor agents. It may cause precipitate labour. Side effects, some serious, are reported in adult women who have taken it to procure abortions. Modern systems of reporting on deaths and side effects have been invaluable in taking dangerous herbal 'medicines' out of use, but their control is still far less strict than it is for prescription medicines.

March

8

9

10

11

12

13

14

Podophyllum peltatum – May apple or American mandrake: from warts to cancers

This North American plant has pretty flowers followed by little berries hiding under its leaves. Lindley describes the rhizome as being a 'very sure and active cathartic [a purgative]', but that the leaves are poisonous and the whole plant narcotic. Austin reports that the ripe fruits were eaten by the Cherokee, Ojibwa, Iroquis and others, but that the roots are highly poisonous and were eaten to commit suicide, and in smaller doses as a purgative. Extracts from the roots were used by the Cherokee to treat intestinal worms – in a dose which was more poisonous to the latter than the patient. The Menomini used it as an insecticide and the Penobscot to cure warts. This latter cytotoxic action was noted by Robert Bentley in 1861 at King's College and a poultice from the roots was, for a while, used to treat cancers that had broken through the skin. An extract of the roots, podophyllin, is still used to treat venereal warts, and the semi-synthetic derivatives etoposide and teniposide, valuable treatments for various cancers, have been produced from it.

March

15

_____

16

_____

17

_____

18

_____

19

_____

20

_____

21

_____

Sanguinaria canadensis – bloodroot or Indian paint: a very powerful cosmetic

A monotypic genus in Papaveraceae (poppy family) from North America, it was initially called *Chelidonium majus canadense acaulon* as the leaves and colourful sap were reminiscent of *Chelidonium majus*, the European greater celandine. Native Americans – Chicksaw, Creek, Seminole, Cherokee and Timacua – used the orange sap as a dye for painting heads and garments, and this may be the origin of the name 'Redskins'. Creek and Yuchi women (red spot on each cheek for Yuchi) painted their faces red if they wished to grant sexual favours. Ponca men put it on their hands and shook hands with a woman to get her to marry them in five to six days. It had multiple medicinal uses but is very toxic if ingested. It contains benzylisoquinoline alkaloids – chiefly sanguinarine – which are both toxic and have the potential to cause fetal abnormalities, but are being investigated as possible anti-cancer drugs. We grow the double form *S. canadensis* f. *multiplex* 'Plena'.

March

22

23

24

25

26

27

28

Paris quadrifolia – herb paris: much misunderstood

This dramatic plant was also known as one-berry and, because of the shape of the four leaves resembling a Burgundian cross or a true love-knot, it was also known as herb true love. Prosaically, the name 'paris' stems from the Latin 'pars' meaning 'equal', referring to the four equal leaves and not to the city or the lover of Helen of Troy. Sixteenth-century herbalists such as Fuchs, who calls it *Aconitum pardaliances*, which means leopard's bane, and Lobel who calls it *Solanum tetraphyllum*, attributed the poisonous properties of *Aconitum* to it. The latter, called monkshood and wolfsbane, are well known as poisonous garden plants. Johnson, however, reports that Lobel fed it to animals and it did them no harm, and caused the recovery of a dog poisoned deliberately with arsenic and mercury, while another dog, which did not receive herb paris, died. It was recommended thereafter as an antidote to poisons, but modern authors report the berry to be toxic. That one poison acted as an antidote to another was a common, if incorrect, belief in the days of herbal medicine.

March

29

30

31

Notes

Viola odorata – the sweet violet: for scorpion stings and litmus paper

We also grow the ornamental double form. Dioscorides mixed the leaves with crushed barley to make a plaster for heartburn, inflamed eyes, and anal prolapse, and used the flowers for sore throats and epilepsy in children. Herbal medicines were used to treat countless different ailments, and in Chinese herbal medicine this belief persists. Violets remained very popular for a multitude of treatments in the 16th and 17th centuries, later writers noting that they caused diarrhoea. Crushed violets applied to the head were advised for 'Melancholy, and dullnesse and heavinesse of the Spirite'; and the seeds, drunk in wine, against the stinging of scorpions, by Lyte. One wonders how many scorpion stings occurred in England in the 16th century. The seeds are toxic causing severe gastroenteritis, with respiratory and circulatory depression, so best avoided even if one is stung by a scorpion. The blue-coloured syrup of the flowers can be used like litmus paper according to Woodville, turning pink with the addition of acid and turning to green with alkali.

April

1

2

3

4

5

6

7

Paeonia officinalis – peony: how are the mighty fallen

The glorious peony commemorates Paeon, physician to the gods of ancient Greece, who enjoyed the best private practice of the era. See Homer's *Iliad* v 401 and 899 (*circa* 800 BC) for further details. The roots, hung round the neck, were regarded as a cure for epilepsy by Galen (in 200 AD) according to Fuchs and Lobel, a belief which was incomprehensible until one finds, in Elizabeth Blackwell's *A curious herbal* (1737), that it was used for febrile fits in teething children. Nailing a brick to a wall would have been just as effective, as febrile fits are self limiting and stop when the fever subsides. Dioscorides used it for uterine disorders, jaundice, kidney disease, cystitis and diarrhoea (a piece of root the size of an almond, boiled in wine, and drunk), and the seeds for stomach problems. He did not use it for epilepsy. Woodville found it of 'no use whatsoever' and Lindley does not even mention it as a treatment for epilepsy. A tincture of the root, in 25% alcohol, of the Chinese *Paeonia lactiflora* has been licensed for general sale under the Traditional Herbal Registration scheme, despite lack of safety data or proof of efficacy, for menopausal flushing.

April

8

9

10

11

12

13

14

Borago officinalis – borage, the star flower: not for your Pimms

Borage is not mentioned in Beck's translation of Dioscorides but from the account of the properties it appears that the 16th century herbalists confusingly called it *buglossum*, a name now used for *Anchusa italica*. Good illustrations are worth a thousand words in identifying plants, especially when the latter are written in Greek or Latin. Ruellio illustrates borage, captioning it as *buglossum*, noting that the Greeks called it *corago*, which had been corrupted to *borago*. He states that Dioscorides wrote that a three-branched plant of borage with root and seed would cure a Tertian fever, and a four-branched plant a Quaternary fever; added to wine it was an aphrodisiac. This is not in Beck and does not sound like Dioscorides. Lyte follows Fuchs who regarded *buglossum* as the same as borage, writing that the flowers and leaves put in wine 'will cause men to be glad and merry, and driveth away all heavy sadness and melancholy'. It was formerly added to the alcoholic drink, Pimms, with oranges and cucumber. It is suspected of being hepatotoxic when eaten, and is genotoxic and carcinogenic. It should not be taken internally.

April

15

16

17

18

19

20

21

Illicium anisatum (illustrated) and *Illicium verum* – star anise: from spice to antiviral

The star-shaped seed pods give these two plants their common name, but they are very different. *Illicium anisatum*, Japanese star anise, contains nasty neurotoxins. It should not be confused with *Illicium verum*, Chinese star anise, a culinary spice also used to make star anise tea. *Illicium* seed pods (mostly from *I. verum*) contain shikimic acid from which 'Tamiflu' (oseltamivir), a treatment for bird and swine flu, is made. Neither extracts from the plants nor shikimic acid itself have any effect as antiviral agents. These plants are also the source of an anti-cancer treatment that is an angioneogenesis inhibitor (ie it stops the production of the blood supply to the tumour). This property is also used to prevent the little tubes, the 'stents' that are used to open up blocked coronary arteries, from clogging up. The stent is impregnated with the chemical and this leaches out slowly, acting like anti-fouling paint and so preventing the coronary artery lining from growing inside the stent.

April

22

_____

23

_____

24

_____

25

_____

26

_____

27

_____

28

_____

Drimys winteri var. *chilensis* – Winter's bark: early cure for scurvy

This tall evergreen tree with panicles of pale green-white flowers in the spring is the source of one of the earliest effective medicines to come from the New World. It grows in Tierra del Fuego and its properties were discovered by Captain John Winter, in charge of the pinnacle *Elizabeth*. He sailed with Francis Drake down the Atlantic to Cape Horn. Here they were separated in a storm and each thought the other lost. Drake went on in the *Golden Hind* to raid Spanish shipping and circumnavigate the globe (1577–80), but Winter returned to England. While off Cape Horn his crew were afflicted with scurvy, but recovered by drinking a soup made from the bitter bark of this tree, on the advice of the local people. This is curious as it is unlikely that they had ever seen scurvy. *Drimys winteri* came to be known as Winter's Bark and vitamin C used to be synthesised from it. Sir Hans Sloane, president of the Royal College of Physicians, and Dr John Fothergill FRCP, were responsible for it being properly described in 1691 and 1768 respectively.

April

29

30

Notes

Halesia carolina – the snowdrop or silverbell tree: commemorating a busy doctor of divinity

This small tree from the Carolinas of North America, with its beautiful white bell-shaped flowers in the spring, commemorates the Reverend Stephen Hales (1677–1761), perpetual curate of Teddington, Middlesex, and fellow of the Royal Society, who was the first man to measure blood pressure. He tied a horse to a gate, put a trochar into its femoral artery, and connected it using the trachea of a goose (in the absence of rubber tubing) to a vertical glass tube, and observed the rise and fall of pressure. After this he gave up vivisection. He was also the first man to measure sap pressure in trees, attaching a manometer to the stump of a recently cut tree and showing that the sap was forced up under pressure, and not merely sucked up by evaporation from the leaves. This he published in *Vegetable Staticks* in 1727. He wrote on temperance (a favourite theme of the modern RCP), anatomy and the circulation of the blood and invented a method of artificial ventilation, but this was of closed spaces and mine-shafts, not artificial respiration. He also invented the surgical forceps.

May

1 _____

2 _____

3 _____

4 _____

5 _____

6 _____

7 _____

Smyrnium olusatrum – Alexanders or great parsley: just a vegetable

This is a truly ancient vegetable, brought to England by the Romans, but now a hedgerow weed in many parts of Britain. *Olus* means a 'pot herb' or vegetable; *atrum* means black, referring to the black seeds. The name is derived from Smyrna, a city in western Turkey founded by Alexander the Great (356–323 BC) from whom it reputedly gains its common name.

Theophrastus noted that the sap was bitter and tasted like myrrh. The leaves and stalks should be boiled and eaten with fish, and the roots pickled or served raw as a salad, according to Dioscorides. The leaves are like celery and the roots like parsnips, according to Mabberley. Lindley reported it as good for flatulence. Culpeper recommended it as a diuretic, for expelling the placenta, 'opening a stoppage of the liver and spleen' (whatever this might mean) and for snake bite.

May

8

9

10

11

12

13

14

Symphytum officinale – comfrey, knit bone, solidago: a liver poison

This exists on one of the oldest plant paintings, the Johnson papyrus, a fragment of a 5th-century Greek codex from Egypt. The plant contains pyrrolizidine alkaloids which are liver poisons. Hepatic cirrhosis has been reported in low dose regular users, and liver damage in a baby whose mother drank comfrey tea. Occasionally it causes acute hepatic venous occlusion with massive, fatal, liver damage. It is also genotoxic and carcinogenic. Neither Pliny nor Dioscorides recommended it for internal use; Galen, however, does, and this was continued by Dodoens and his translators, but not by Fuchs. All recommend the crushed roots or leaves applied as a poultice to heal wounds. Culpeper, regrettably, recommended comfrey tea for almost everything. It is still widely used in herbal medicine, but in the UK it has been removed from all licensed products intended for internal use, being permitted only as an ingredient for products intended for external use on unbroken skin. Beware.

May

15

16

17

18

19

20

21

Chelidonium majus – the greater celandine: yellow flowers for jaundice

No relation to the lesser celandine, *Ranunculus ficaria*, it has yellow flowers and yellow sap, which, according to the Doctrine of Signatures, indicated that it should be good for jaundice. Dioscorides recommended it for this, for shingles, toothache and for improving sight. Called swallow-wort ('chelidonium' is Greek for a 'swallow') because it grows when swallows appear and withers when they leave. It was also thought to recover the sight of blind fledgling swallows. According to Aristotle, quoted by Johnson, the eyes of newborn swallows are immature ('not fledge') and 'if a man do pricke them out, do grow againe, and afterwards do perfectly recover their sight' even without the use of this herb. This is an interesting observation on the potential of stem cells, if true. It was used in the College's *Pharmacopoeia Londinensis* of 1618. Lindley recommended it for curing opacities in the cornea, despite noting that the yellow sap was a violent acrid poison and a popular remedy for treating warts. In recent years it was still being used, crushed and made into a gargle, for toothache. Its sale is legally restricted because of hepatotoxicity, reported by the World Health Authority.

May

22

_____

23

_____

24

_____

25

_____

26

_____

27

_____

28

_____

Papaver rhoeas – corn poppy: cheerful sedative

This is the scarlet poppy of our fields and First World War battlefields. Dioscorides recommended that six seed heads boiled in 140 ml of wine would help one sleep. Culpeper wrote 'Poppy seeds ease pain and provoke sleep. Your best way is to make an emulsion of them with barley water'. It seems that its opium content may be responsible. The name 'rhoeas' comes from the Greek 'to drop off', apparently referring to the petals that do not last long rather than the vernacular for falling asleep. It was used in the College's *Pharmacopoeia Londinensis* of 1618, and a syrup of the flowers was still recommended as a cough suppressant in the edition of 1793 – as *Papaver erraticum*.

The petals were also used to make a sedative syrup for children, according to Sowerby's *English botany*, vol 5 (1818), but this states that poppy seeds contain no opium. However, modern studies have shown that they do contain morphine. Poppy seed bagels from *Papaver somniferum* contain enough opium to be detected, if eaten, on urine testing.

May

29

30

31

Notes

Pulsatilla vulgaris – Pasque (Easter) flower, wind flower, bastard anemone: just elegant

Lindley and Woodville knew this as *Anemone pulsatilla*, the common name being Pasque (Easter) flower. At the end of the 18th century it was recommended for blindness, cataracts, syphilis, strokes and much more, treatments which, as was clear to physicians at the time, were valueless. Johnson writes: 'They serve only for the adorning of gardens and garlands, being floures of great beauty'. It is in the buttercup family, Ranunculaceae, all members of which are poisonous. It was recommended, by mouth, for 'obstinate case of taenia' (tapeworms). One hopes it was more toxic to the worm than the patient. Flowers with a central disc and radiating florets were regarded as being good for eye complaints under the Doctrine of Signatures. Porta writes (translated): 'Argemone [*Papaver argemone*], and anemone, have flowers of this shape, from this they cure ulcers and cloudiness of the cornea'. There were occupational diseases even before there were words like pneumoconiosis, and Lindley writes that 'the powder of the root causes itching of the eyes, colic and vomiting, if in pulverising it the operator do not avoid the fine dust which is driven up'.

June

1 _____

2 _____

3 _____

4 _____

5 _____

6 _____

7 _____

Cistus ladanifer – gum rockrose: a fragrant resin

The common gum cistus is from south west Europe and north Africa. The fragrant resin from the sticky leaves, gum labdanum, is extracted and used in Mediterranean regions as an insecticide and deodorant. Collecting the resin was done with a rake, the tines (prongs) of which were made of strips of leather. The bushes were raked and when enough resin had accumulated on the tines, this was scraped off – an arduous business that was undertaken in the heat of the Mediterranean midday sun. Stories that it was collected from the beards of goats were also put about by Greek monks, but modern techniques involve distillation of the leaves.

Dodoens advises local application to prevent hair loss and cure earache; to remove scars; and on the chest to alleviate coughs. The fumes from leaves burnt on hot coals were said to cure uterine disorders. Johnson adds that the fumes were also useful for expelling the placenta. In Lindley's time it was recommended for chronic catarrh and as a stimulant.

June

8

9

10

11

12

13

14

Listera ovata – the common twayblade: honours a fellow of the RCP

This rather dull, green-flowered orchid is found throughout northern Europe and Asia and in North America (on an island in Lake Huron, Ontario). It grows in great numbers in open fields and light woodland, where it is pollinated by *Cantharis rufipes* beetles. It was used for treating wounds and ruptures (Dodoens, Fuchs, Johnson) but does not appear in modern medical herbals.

Robert Brown named it after Dr Martin Lister FRCP (1638–1712), physician to Queen Anne (see *Munk's Roll* vol 1: 442 (1878)). He published a description of around 1,000 shells in 1685, and numerous papers on spiders and geology as well as making significant contributions to the Ashmolean Museum. His orchid first appeared as *Ophris* in Leonard Fuchs' herbal *De Historia Stirpium* (1542) and as 'Twayblade' in Henry Lyte's translation of Dodoens' *A nieve herball* (1578). Dodoens grouped it with the bird's nest orchid *Neottia nidus-avis*; Linnaeus called it *Ophrys ovata* (1753), but recently taxonomists have agreed with Dodoens and have re-classified it as *Neottia ovata*.

June

15

_____

16

_____

17

_____

18

_____

19

_____

20

_____

21

_____

Digitalis lanata – the woolly foxglove: for the heart

This, the 'Grecian' foxglove of Eastern Europe, is the source of the cardiac medicine digoxin. The use of the dried leaves of the purple foxglove, *D. purpurea*, for treating heart failure (then called 'dropsy', referring to the oedema which causes the legs, and occasionally the whole body, to swell up) was discovered by Dr William Withering after nine years of testing on his charity patients, and described in 1785 in *An account of the foxglove*. *Digitalis purpurea* contains many cardioactive glycosides which increase the efficiency of the heart, and the leaves were used until single chemicals, such as digoxin, were extracted from the leaves of *D. lanata*. Digoxin has the advantage of purity and not varying in strength according to the time of year. Withering recognised the toxic side effects of foxglove, including xanthopsia (objects appear yellow), slow heart rate, vomiting and diarrhoea. In the Medicinal Garden in the summer, *Digitalis lanata* is visited by little *Anthophora* bees which become stuporose and lie upside down in the flowers, seemingly unable to fly away when disturbed.

June

22

23

24

25

26

27

28

Carpobrotus acinaciformis – Hottentot fig: traditional South African medicine

This pretty mesembryanthemum with fleshy leaves and daisy-like flowers comes from the Western Cape of South Africa, but is a common seaside plant in southern England. It thrives in full sun and a well-drained soil.

In South African 'muthi' medicine, the sap is used as a gargle for sore throats; for burns; eczema; tuberculosis; dysentery; toothache; thrush; stomach upsets and wounds. The fruit of the yellow-flowered, related species, *C. edulis*, also known as Hottentot fig, is made into a jam and put in curries. The sap is mucilaginous and when applied to a burn probably works by drying to provide a thin protective layer, preventing bacteria from reaching the burnt surface. Infection of burns is the commonest problem in their management and while in modern medicine an aerosol spray of a varnish-like material is used, the saps of various plants, including the aloes, are staple domestic remedies.

June

29

30

Notes

Hypericum perforatum – St John's wort: not a herbal remedy for depression

It is so named because it flowers around St John's day (24 June), 'wort' is the early English word for a plant, and *H. perforatum* because of the translucent pores in the leaves. Coles wrote that these pores indicated that it was good for skin conditions. Lyte calls it Fugam Demonum which Fuchs explains arose from a superstitious belief that it could drive out demons. It was used as a diuretic, for bladder stone, inducing menstruation, for fevers, sciatica, burns, wounds and skin ulcers. Woodville wrote that 'the ancients' used it for hysteria, hypochondriasis and mania, but early herbals do not support this or that it was ever used for depression. By the beginning of the 19th century it had virtually fallen out of use, Lindley reporting only that it 'has been used in gargles and lotions'. It is only licensed for use in 'slightly low mood and mild anxiety' and is now contraindicated in depression. Side effects include photosensitivity (even cows that eat it get sunburn) and enhancement of inactivation of warfarin, oral contraceptives, HIV treatments and immunosuppressants, and a huge range of other medicines, by inducing drug metabolising enzymes in the liver. Tell your doctor if you are taking it...

July

1

2

3

4

5

6

7

Atropa belladonna – deadly or greater nightshade: useful medicine, complex poison

In the family Solanaceae, it is a bush with small brown, tubular flowers and bright black berries, also known as dwale or *Mandragora theophrastis*. It is named after Atropos, the eldest of the three Fates. Her sisters, Lachesis and Clotho, spun the web of life and measured it respectively; Atropos cut it. Belladonna, Italian for 'beautiful lady', as Italian ladies used the distilled juice as a cosmetic to preserve their youth and beauty. All parts of it contain tropane alkaloids, principally atropine, hyoscyamine and scopolamine. These are used medicinally to dilate the pupil; as a pre-medication to dry up bronchial secretions and to speed up the heart rate – none of which is recorded in early herbals. It is an antidote to organophosphorus nerve gas poisoning. Historically the leaves were smoked for asthma and applied as an analgesic poultice to fungating cancers. Larger doses cause hallucinations and coma. It was used to induce unconsciousness for operations before anaesthetics were available. The berries do not taste unpleasant, but all parts of it are poisonous and best avoided.

July

8

9

10

11

12

13

14

Inula helenium – elecampane, scabwort: 'good against scabs and itch'

This hardy perennial, with its huge coarse leaves and sunflower-like flowers, is a native to Europe and west Asia. The roots and bark were authorised for use in medicine in the first *Pharmacopoeia* published by the College in 1618. Culpeper wrote that it was 'wholesome for the stomach, resists poison, helps old coughs and shortness of breath, helps ruptures and provokes lust; in ointments it is good against scabs and itch' and was 'one of the most beneficial roots nature affords for the help of the consumptive'. Woodville reported that it was used for 'dyspepsia, pulmonary affections and uterine obstructions' but he had not seen any evidence that it actually worked.

It contains sesquiterpene lactones which can cause allergies and irritation. The roots, flowers and oil are still used by modern herbalists for chest complaints and digestive disorders. Helen of Troy – hence the name *helenium* – carried the flowers with her when abducted by Paris, according to Johnson. Fuchs reports a legend that the plant arose from her tears.

July

15

16

17

18

19

20

21

Brugmansia suaveolens – Angel's trumpets: decorative, medicinal and toxic

This is another plant within the family Solanaceae – from the Andes of South America. It is a highly decorative, night-fragrant shrub. All parts of the plant contain high levels of scopolamine, one of the chemicals responsible for the toxic effects of deadly nightshade, *Atropa belladonna*.

Rubbing a flower will transfer sufficient alkaloid on to one's fingers to dilate the pupil if one uses these fingers to rub one's eye, and Lewis reports that sufficient can be absorbed through the skin, by rubbing with the leaves, to induce coma. The leaves or flowers are made into a tea, or smoked, and while the coma and hallucinations may last 24 hours (perhaps more), dilated pupils may persist for a week. A worker at the RCP, who had spent 14 hours in a coma followed by visual hallucinations after such a tea, said nothing would induce him to try it again. Death usually occurs because the intoxicated person is left alone and falls or drowns. Italians, unable to obtain tobacco during the war, used to smoke the dried leaves, and plants may still be seen growing beside maize fields in Tuscany for this purpose. Best avoided.

July

22

23

24

25

26

27

28

Lobelia tupa – Chilean cardinal flower: for toothache

The leaves of *Lobelia tupa*, which has fiery red flower scapes, were smoked by the Mapuchu Indians of Chile for their rather special effects (definitely not recommended). In addition to being narcotic it was used to relieve toothache. The genus was named after Matthias de L'Obel, Flemish botanist and physician to James I of England, author of the beautifully illustrated herbal, *Plantarum seu Stirpium Historia* (1576). We also grow the scarlet *Lobelia cardinalis* and the sky-blue *Lobelia siphilitica*. The latter was sold by North American Indians as a 'secret cure' to gullible British colonists, who desperately wanted a remedy for syphilis. John Lindley noted 'European practice does not confirm its American reputation'.

The plant contains lobeline, a piperidine alkaloid, which activates nicotinic acetylcholine receptors (in the same way as tobacco), stimulates the central nervous system regulation of respiration and is a bronchodilator. It has been used as a nicotine substitute to help tobacco withdrawal. In the past it was used for asthma, bronchitis and whooping cough, but is no longer regarded as a safe medicine for these conditions.

July

29

30

31

Notes

Taxus baccata – European yew: useful in chemotherapy

Although regarded as poisonous since Theophrastus, Johnson and his school friends used to eat the red berries without harm. Johnson clearly ate the fleshy arils and spat out the seed, which is as poisonous as the leaves. It is a source of taxol, an important chemotherapeutic agent for breast and other cancers. It was first extracted from the bark of *T. brevifolia*, the Pacific yew tree, in 1966. About 1,100 kg of bark produces 10 g of taxol, and 360,000 trees a year would have been required for the needs of the USA – an unsustainable amount. In 1990 a precursor of taxol was produced from the needles of the European yew so saving the Pacific trees. It is now produced in fermentation tanks from cell cultures of *Taxus*. Curiously, there is a fungus, *Nodulisporium sylviforme*, which lives on the yew tree, that also produces taxol. Because taxol stops cell division, it is used in the stents that are inserted to keep coronary arteries open. Here it inhibits – in a different way, but like anti-fouling paint on the bottom of ships – the overgrowth of endothelial cells that would otherwise eventually block the tube.

August

1

2

3

4

5

6

7

Catharanthus roseus – Madagascar periwinkle: a cure for leukaemia

From this pan-tropical weed, vinblastine (in 1958) and vincristine (in 1979), effective medications for leukaemia, lymphomas and some solid tumours were isolated. With combined treatment, cure rates of 70% were achieved in what were, previously, invariably fatal diseases. They work by blocking cell division by binding to tubulin, the protein that forms the spindle during metaphase. This was discovered by investigators looking for a cure for diabetes when they tested this plant, which was widely used for this in the West Indies, drunk as a tea. The plant also contains numerous physiologically active chemicals including the indole alkaloids, catharanthine and vindoline, which lower blood sugar.

The vincristine content of this plant is a mere 0.0003 g/100 g, so 2 kg of leaf are required to produce sufficient vincristine (6 mg) for a single course of treatment for a child. Fortunately it is a vigorous weed and easy to grow in the tropics. Artificial synthesis of vinblastine was achieved in 1979, of vincristine in 2004.

August

8 _____

9 _____

10 _____

11 _____

12 _____

13 _____

14 _____

Helianthus annuus – marigold of Peru: food for lust

More commonly called sunflower, or historically, floure of the sun. It was much recommended by Johnson as the buds, covered in flour, boiled and eaten with butter, vinegar and pepper, far surpass artichokes 'in procuring bodily lust'! Sadly, today only the seeds of sunflower are consumed, as the source of sunflower oil used in cooking. It contains mono and polyunsaturated fats, linoleic acid and oleic acid, and is low in saturated fats. As such it helps lower cholesterol and so the risk of heart disease, but it may increase the risk of breast and prostatic cancer. It is a rich source of vitamin E. It is not in Fuchs, but is elegantly illustrated in Lobel as *Solis flos* and *Chrysanthemum peruvianum*. Hybridising and selective breeding can reduce the level of saturated fats even further, as well as producing scarlet flowers like this cultivar. Darwin's 'natural selection' has been replaced by 'artificial selection' as the commonest cause of new varieties of plant.

August

15

16

17

18

19

20

21

Cucurbita maxima – pumpkin or squash; a vermifuge

We grow the 200-year-old cultivar 'Golden Hubbard' whose seed has been conserved by the Amish of Pennsylvania, USA. The rind is very thick, but the taste is delicious.

We also grow the sister gourd, *Cucurbita pepo*, one of the oldest cultivated plants, first grown 11,000 years ago in Mexico, but extinct in the wild. Varieties are selectively bred for their taste, colour and shape. The seeds, ground to a powder, were used to kill intestinal tape-worms (please note that there are safer remedies). The two species *C. pepo* and *C. maxima* were cross-pollinated in the Garden and the following year all our saved seeds produced a bevy of hybrids.

It is not easy to tell if it is the 'Apple of Coloquintada' or the 'Pompions' of Johnson, but as many of these were cultivated plants, they may all be varieties of *Cucurbita*. The woodcuts are helpful and suggest that Johnson knew it as *Pepo major sylvestris* – the great wild pompion.

August

22

23

24

25

26

27

28

Vitex agnus-castus – monks' pepper, the chaste plant: an anti-aphrodisiac

This buddleia-like shrub comes from Sicily but is hardy in much of the British Isles. It was known as the chaste plant, and reported by Woodville that, being 'especially useful to those living a monastic life these seeds have been called Monks' Pepper' and were sprinkled on food to prevent carnal thoughts. Lyte says it is 'a singular remedy for such as would live chaste, for it withstandeth all uncleanliness and the filthy desire to lechery'. Nuns carried the leaves in their pockets to keep their minds pure, believing that its virtuous properties could be absorbed – like the copper in the bangles for arthritis worn to this day. Visitors to the garden report that it is still found growing outside the monasteries of France. It continues to be used in herbal medicine for premenstrual syndromes although clinical effectiveness is not supported by controlled trials. It does have dopaminergic activity and may lower serum prolactin levels.

August

29

30

31

Notes

Hyoscyamus niger – black henbane: small amounts medicinal, more is poison
Black henbane (also known in past centuries as apollinaris and fabasuilla) was recognised by Johnson and Lyte as being poisonous, and while alleviating pain, caused sleep that could be fatal both if drunk or if the skin was washed with a decoction of it. The ability for poisons in plants to be absorbed through the skin is little known in this modern age. *Hyoscyamus* species contain the same tropane alkaloids as *Atropa belladonna*, deadly nightshade, and give their name to hyoscyamine and hyoscine, the latter used as a premedication before surgical operations. Used in a poultice it appears to have a local analgesic effect. It was recommended for gout, mastalgia, sore eyes and ureteric stones, but the dangers of it and its merely temporary benefits were well known. Only Dioscorides, Galen (according to Fuchs who reports this) and Turner recognised that it could cause madness (by which they must be referring to the hallucinations it can cause) and advised against its use. Turner recommended smoking the leaves for a cough. The yellow henbane *Hyoscyamus luteolus*, of Lobel is *Nicotiana rustica* and not the yellow-flowered *Hyoscyamus albus*.

September

1

2

3

4

5

6

7

Ricinus communis – castor oil plant: purgative and umbrella poison

This was known as Palma Christi, or Figuera di l'inferno (the fig from hell) according to Lobel. The coat of the seed of this plant from Southern Europe and North Africa is the source of the poison ricin, best known for the umbrella murder in 1978 when the Bulgarian secret service was alleged to have killed Georgi Markov with a pellet containing ricin (although none was found), using an air gun disguised as an umbrella, on Waterloo Bridge in London. The seeds also produce castor oil (which does not contain ricin), formerly used as a laxative. The leaves are used worldwide as a herbal remedy for stomach complaints. Woodville describes at length how castor oil is extracted, but neither he nor Lindley mention that the seeds are poisonous. Lyte says that the oil, then known as *Oleum cicinum*, was good for rubbing on the skin, and the leaves for swollen eyes and erysipelas, but that the seed makes one vomit 'with much payne and greefe'. Two seeds ingested are said to be fatal, but vomiting as a reaction to poisons protects the unwary.

September

8

9

10

11

12

13

14

Dichroa febrifuga – fever bush: anti-malarial to sleeping pill

Used in Chinese medicine for treating fevers, it was found, in 1948, to contain a compound called beta-dichroine in the dried roots, which had potent anti-malarial activity. An identical chemical, which came to be called febrifugine, was isolated from the leaves of garden hydrangeas. It proved to be 64–100 times more potent than quinine as an anti-malarial in animals, but equally more toxic. Trials on prisoners in Texas, and on patients in Mexico, showed that it caused such persistent vomiting and hepatotoxicity in effective doses that it was unusable, and in doses that were tolerated it was ineffective. Ever-resourceful pharmacists synthesised a tolyl derivative, which was found to be a mild hypnotic ('short acting, no hangover, no side-effects' etc, as the drug reps used to tell the junior doctors of my day over a steak supper), and marketed in the mid-1960s as methaqualone, an ingredient of the sleeping tablet 'Mandrax', which quickly became the drug abuse of choice for getting a 'high'. It was almost as quickly banned by most countries. Illegal manufacture continues in South Africa where methaqualone powder is mixed with cannabis and smoked.

September

15

16

17

18

19

20

21

Punica granatum – pomegranate: fertility, wealth, intestinal worms and an ink

The fruit was known as *Granatum malum*, the flowers as balustines and its myriad ruby-coloured seeds associate it with fertility and wealth. The RCP has had it on its coat of arms, granted by Henry VIII, since 1546, as it 'cured burning agues' according to the published history of the RCP. Dioscorides writes that it is unsuitable for fevers, but Parkinson recommended it. The suggestion that it was taken from the arms of Catherine of Aragon, who married Henry VIII in 1509 (divorced 1533, died 1536), is an unlikely alternative. The bark was used by Dioscorides and the 16th-century herbalists to treat intestinal worms, for which it is still used in South Africa (but its side effects are dangerous). Parkinson also tells us that it makes ' the best sort of writing inke, which is durable to the world's end'. A mouthwash of the flowers treated mouth ulcers and bad gums. Dioscorides, who does not advocate it for much in the medicinal line, believed that eating three flowers protected one from bleary eyes for a year.

September

22

23

24

25

26

27

28

Dahlia merckii – Mexican dahlia – the future direction of therapeutics?

This wild species of the well-known garden plant comes from Mexico. It represents, in the Medicinal Garden, the possible future of medicine. It does not suffer from mildew because it contains a gene that gives it resistance to fungal infections. The fungal-resistance gene from *D merckii* has been experimentally inserted into the mildew-prone aubergine, to give healthy crops that do not need spraying with fungicides. Many of the illnesses that affect humankind are due to defective genes, from cystic fibrosis and schizophrenia to diabetes and atherosclerosis. If these defective genes can be replaced by genes that do not carry these diseases, medicine will have made a step forward that will dwarf all past progress. Making transgenic plants is complicated and has many opponents. Inserting 'healthy' genes into people is much more difficult, but – one hopes – will be possible and welcomed when it happens. We can look forward to the day when we will regard insulin for diabetes and major tranquilisers for schizophrenia with the same condescending scorn that we have for the Doctrine of Signatures and copper bangles for arthritis.

September

29

_____

30

_____

Notes

_____

_____

_____

_____

_____

_____

Senna corymbosa – senna: dangerous purgative

This beautiful shrub that flowers from midsummer until the frosts of winter, is the source of one of the best known of all herbal medicines – senokot (and senna pods and senna tea), introduced to European medicine by the Arabians. Every part of the plant contains anthraquinones which, if taken internally, act as a powerful laxative to treat constipation by stimulating the nerve cells of the large bowel. Johnson notes 'it is a singular purging medicine' with over a page on its uses.

   When used regularly the nerves to the large bowel may be destroyed, leaving a permanently dilated large bowel that never functions properly again. This is a plant which causes the condition it treats to become permanent. Additionally, with prolonged use, the lining of the bowel turns black, serum potassium levels may fall, resulting in cardiac irregularities and sometimes death. Coma, neuropathy and hepatitis have also been reported. It is advertised on television and is available without prescription or health warning against long-term use. What do you think? Lyte recommends it strongly for depression, but one might claim to be cured rather than take it again.

October

1 _____

2 _____

3 _____

4 _____

5 _____

6 _____

7 _____

Glaucium flavum – yellow horned poppy: no opium in this one

Identifying the plants used two thousand years ago is often difficult as few illustrations have come down to us. The oral tradition sufficed until the invention of printing and the massive use of woodcuts in the herbals of Fuchs, Dodoens, Lobel and others from the 16th century onwards. Names used by the ancient herbalists were perpetuated by Linnaeus when he introduced the binomial system of plant names in 1753, for it was called *Glaucium* by Dioscorides in the first century AD. Lyte calls it *Papaver corniculatum*, Fuchs uses *Mekone ceratite* ('mekone' being Greek for poppy), but the earlier name has been perpetuated.

The roots were used 'to provoke urine, unstoppeth the liver' and for 'greefe in their raynes', which may be interpreted as 'kidney pain'. The seeds were used as a purgative, and the leaves and flowers as a poultice for cleaning old sores. The principal active alkaloid is glaucine, which suppresses cough and may cause lowering of blood pressure and hallucinations. It does not appear to have opium-like activity and is not used in modern medicine.

October

8

9

10

11

12

13

14

Camellia sinensis – tea: just tea

Only marginally hardy, this small shrub seems happy in the Medicinal Garden. The leaves are the source of tea, drunk principally for its stimulating effect. This is due mainly to its caffeine content with small amounts of theophylline and theobromine. The dry leaf contains more caffeine than coffee, but less of it by weight is used in making a cup, so tea as a beverage is less stimulating. The various different types of tea – black, green and white – have their different flavours due solely to the preparation method and the quality of the leaf. It was unknown to the 16th-century herbalists, coming as it did from China. Tea was first brought to Europe in 1610 and by 1750 had become the British national drink with 18,000 tonnes imported annually. Most tea was grown in China until Robert Fortune brought 25,000 plants and half a dozen tea manufacturers to the Himalayas in the middle of the 19th century, after which it became one of India's principal exports. Worldwide, 3.5 million tonnes of tea are now harvested annually.

October

15

16

17

18

19

20

21

Plumbago auriculata – Cape leadwort, plumbago: for toothache

The woodcut of *Plumbago* in Johnson is of *Plumbago europaea* which (he writes) was known by Pliny as *Molybdaena* or *Plumbago*, by others *Lepidium* and *Dentaria* (although in Matthioli these are other genera) and not this scandent South African shrub. The genus name derives from the Latin for lead, but modern authors differ as to whether it was used as a treatment of lead poisoning or that when it was used for eye conditions the skin turned the colour of lead – observations not noted by the 16th-century herbalists. Lewis states that the root can be used for toothache and that it contains plumbagin which has antibacterial properties. Johnson pre-dated him by 400 years as his sole recommendation is for toothache, which might be assumed from the name *Dentaria*. He warns that the sap is very corrosive and will raise blisters on a man's hand. In South Africa it is used traditionally to treat warts, broken bones and wounds, for headaches and bad dreams.

A year in the Medicinal Garden of the Royal College of Physicians 95

October

22

_____

23

_____

24

_____

25

_____

26

_____

27

_____

28

_____

Platanus orientalis subspecies insularis – Eastern plane tree: Hippocratic plane

In 400 BC, Hippocrates, the Father of Medicine, taught medical students under a plane tree on the island of Cos off the coast of mainland Greece. There is a huge tree there with a circumference of 12 metres, but only 500 years old, which bears a sign that it is the original tree. This is clearly not true, but it may well be a descendant. Seed from this tree was taken to the National Botanic Garden in New York by the distinguished American neurologist, Wilder Penfield, and cuttings from the resulting seedlings were sent to the Royal Botanic Gardens, Kew, and from there one was donated to the RCP in 1965. Another tree, which came via the Chelsea Physic Garden, was planted at the same time but removed when it became too large for the site. Ours may be the largest in the south-east of England. Unlike the London plane tree (of which we have several to the front of the RCP), this has superficial roots that run on the surface of the lawn, making it unsuitable as a street tree. It also has a corrugated bark unlike the London plane's flaking scales.

October

29

30

31

Notes

Tetrapanax papyrifer 'Rex' – rice paper plant: paper and dressings

First described by Hooker in 1852 as *Aralia papyrifera*, this plant in the ginseng (*Panax ginseng*) family is used to make paper, and in the past for surgical dressings. It was used in traditional Chinese medicine as a diuretic, for fevers, as a sedative, and for intestinal worms. Chinese medicine books, and the concepts of much modern herbalism, are as difficult to understand in terms of actual human physiology and pathology as the early European herbals. While such herbal medicine still has its proponents, the dominance of modern medicine is making strong inroads even in the third world. *Tetrapanax* is a dramatic plant of borderline tenderness in the UK and its huge leaves and furry flowers dominate the Asian section of the garden.

Unlike ginseng which has been used, reputedly, since 3,000 BC, it has no claims to be a universal panacea; it was never only the preserve of emperors, nor does it produce such a flurry of scientific papers extolling amazing activities of polysyllabic molecules in doing everything from the induction of choline acetylase in the basal forebrain to potentiating the reticuloendothelial system. It is just a nice plant.

November

1 _____

2 _____

3 _____

4 _____

5 _____

6 _____

7 _____

Capsicum annuum – chilli peppers, salad peppers: culinary, but medicinally promising.

Hundreds of different varieties of chilli peppers and salad peppers are derived from *Capsicum annuum*, brought to Europe by Columbus in the mid-16th century, but believed to have been in cultivation in Bolivia since 7,200 BC. Sixteenth-century herbalists called it *Capsicum*, ginnie or Indian pepper, and used it for scrofula (tuberculous lymph nodes); they write that it kills dogs, believing mistakenly that it was *Zingiber caninum* reported upon by Avicenna in the 10th century. Lindley used it for fevers and sore throat in scarlet fever. It is unlikely that they had tried it for none mention its burning 'taste', except Woodville, who writes that 'the taste is intolerably hot'. The chemical responsible for its 'hotness' is capsaicin, used medically for pain relief, applied locally for muscle injury and post-herpetic neuralgia. It blocks pain transmission peripherally in P2 nerve fibres to the spinal cord. Capsaicin has been shown, experimentally, to kill cancer cells by attacking their mitochondria and to reduce the size of tumours of the pancreas and prostate. It is immensely potent in minute quantities – never rub an eye after touching the cut surface of a chilli pepper!

November

8
_____

9
_____

10
_____

11
_____

12
_____

13
_____

14
_____

Tulbaghia violacea – wild garlic, society garlic: attractive 'muthi' medicine

This is a pretty member of the onion family, Alliaceae, from South Africa. Van Wyck writes that it is used in the traditions of 'muthi' medicine for fevers and colds, asthma and tuberculosis. The fresh bulbs are boiled in water and the decoction taken orally or as an enema. The leaves were used to treat cancer of the oesophagus, but the evidence for this being effective is entirely lacking, although extracts inhibit the growth of cancer cells in laboratory conditions. The leaves and flowers are eaten as a salad. It is hugely important that 'muthi' medicine receives agricultural and scientific help. Wild plants are being exterminated by over-collection for medicinal use in many parts of the world, and if they are of no medicinal value, this is doubly tragic. Proper investigation and propagation of therapeutically useful plants is needed – if cannabis and opium can be grown on an industrial scale then truly medicinal plants need this sort of cultivation as well. It is a very useful addition to the garden because it flowers for most of the year, is fragrant, and survives minus 10°C in the winter and drought in the summer.

A year in the Medicinal Garden of the Royal College of Physicians 103

November

15

16

17

18

19

20

21

Aloe ferox – the Cape aloe: purgative, alcoholic panacea and radiation treatment

The juice of the leaves yields emodin, an anthraquinone which acts on the large intestine as a violent purgative. In South Africa it is also used to treat arthritis, eczema, conjunctivitis, hypertension and stress (van Wyck). It is an ingredient of Swedish Bitters, a panacea (according to the producers) for all ills. The manufacturers give its constituents as 'A mixture of aloe, angelica root, manna, myrrh, camphor, saffron, senna leaves, theriac venezian, carline thistle roots, rhubarb roots, zedoary ... blended with Chamonix fruit spirit of 43 % alcohol and left standing in a warm place for 14 days and shaken daily. This is then strained and bottled'. One might not die of anything else if one consumed enough.

More importantly, like *Aloe vera*, the sap is used in cosmetics and to heal burns. It is said to have been used extensively to treat radiation burns at Hiroshima, and an urban myth claims that the American government stockpiled large quantities in the 1950s in the expectation of a nuclear war.

November

22

23

24

25

26

27

28

Echium vulgare – viper's bugloss: much confused by herbalists

Dioscorides wrote about the purple-flowered *Echium plantagineum*, calling it 'echion' and 'doris'. There are not many plants called 'doris'; others called it alcibiadeion, which is less memorable. Its virtue was to cure bites from vipers and to protect those who had drunk it from being bitten. Taken with wine or porridge, it was said to be good for backache and inducing lactation. Lyte describes the blue flowers of *E. vulgare* calling it vipers' bugloss, 'echion', and *Echium alcibiacum*, noting its similarity to common bugloss (*Anchusa officinalis*). However, the plant he calls *Buglossum magnum* is circium, a thistle. Ruellio divides echion into sylvestre, which is vipers' bugloss, and *Echion domesticum*, which is common bugloss; but his *Buglossum* is borage, *Borago officinalis*. Fuchs renames Dioscorides' echion as *Sylvestre buglossum*; but his bugloss is borage. Johnson's engraving labelled *Echium vulgare*/vipers' buglosse matches our plant, and his *Echium rubro flore*/red-floured vipers' buglosse is Dioscorides' *E. plantagineum*. His '*Buglossum* cowslip' is *Primula veris*. *Echium* is an invasive weed in the USA where it is known as salvation Jane and Patterson's curse. Confused?

November

29

30

Notes

Myrtus communis subspecies tarentina – myrtle: a fair maiden, good for dandruff

Dioscorides recommends the fruit for treating haemoptysis ('spitting blood') and cystitis, and, if boiled, he said it made a fine wine. In various forms it was used as a hair dye, for sore eyes, anal and uterine prolapse, dandruff and shingles, all sorts of inflammations, scorpion bites and even sweaty armpits. Our plant has white berries, but he regarded those with black berries as being more effective (ours do turn black with age). Lyte adds that the juice of the berries kept the hair black and stopped it falling out, and prevented intoxication. He notes that it only flowered in hot summers in England, but it is reliable in flower now, either due to global warming or selection of suitable clones.

According to Lyte, it is named after Merlyne, a fair maiden of Athens in ancient Greece who judged the athletic games. Slain by a disgruntled competitor, the goddess Minerva brought her back as the myrtle tree in perpetual memory. The myrtle tree is also an ancient Jewish symbol for peace and justice. Myrtle wine is still made in Tuscany and now even in China.

December

1

2

3

4

5

6

7

Anthyllis vulneria – **Kidney vetch: for healing wounds and kidney problems**

Beck regards the *Anthyllis* of Dioscorides as *Ajuga iva* and *Cressa cretica*. But the description and woodcut in Lyte, as *Anthyllis prior* or great anthyllis, is of our plant. Both recommend it for pain and difficulty in urinating and renal pain ('it fhall prevayle much againft the hoote piffe, the Strangury or difficultie to make water, and againft the payne of the reynes'); as a pessary for uterine disorders, and for curing wounds. Johnson identifies several plants, none of them *Anthyllis vulneria*, with a woodcut copied from Lobel's *Alsine minor*. With its hairy leaves, often associated with stopping bleeding (the hairs, like cotton wool on a shaving cut, help platelets coagulate), it is not surprising that Linnaeus called it *Anthyllis vulneria*, a 'vulnary' being a herb that acted as a styptic – as Lindley notes. However, this virtue is not noted by any of the early herbalists, so its original identity remains obscure.

December

8

9

10

11

12

13

14

Nicotiana tabacum – tobacco: the world's most poisonous plant

This is truly the most poisonous plant in the world; a death from an illness caused by smoking tobacco occurs once every eight seconds according to the World Health Organization, and is set to double by 2020 as the Chinese increase their smoking habits. Fernando Cortez brought it to Spain from Central America in 1518. It first appeared in a European herbal in Dodoens as *Hyoscyamus peruvianus* or henbane of Peru – he at least realised it was poisonous. Nicholas Monardes in *De hierba panacea* (1571) lists 36 diseases it cured. Lyte, curiously, does not mention it, although Johnson does, writing about how smoking may appear to alleviate illness but does nothing. Lobel calls it *Herba sancta*, placing it between comfrey (*Symphytum*) and *Pulmonaria* rather than with other poisonous plants. As with many new drugs, it received a rapturous reception and then was slated by everyone. Lindley, in giving an example of its poisonous nature, says that the Hottentots put it on the tongue of snakes and they died instantly. A large stick would have been safer. It took over 400 years after its introduction before the full enormity of its long-term effects was realised.

A year in the Medicinal Garden of the Royal College of Physicians   113

December

15

16

17

18

19

20

21

Rosmarinus officinalis – rosemary: a fragrant herb

Rosemary flowers several times a year and is much loved by gardeners for its fragrance. Dioscorides recommended boiling it in water, then drinking it prior to exercise as a cure for jaundice. Ruellio called it *Rosmarinus coronarium* and *libanotis* and Lyte adds that the Arabian physicians say it 'comforteth the brain, the memory and the inward senses, and that sweets made from sugared flowers restore speech if taken daily when fasting'. As speech may recover spontaneously after being lost due to a stroke, one wonders if it was this phenomenon that was being observed. Ashes of rosemary were used for saving loose teeth and making them look pretty. Lindley writes that it relieves headache and stimulates the mind to vigorous action, adding 'It is principally remarkable for its undoubted power of encouraging the growth of hair and curing baldness ... an infusion of it prevents the hair from uncurling in damp weather'. One might even try this. Woodville adds that many people drink it as a tea for breakfast. Traditionally eaten with roast lamb in Britain.

December

22

23

24

25

26

27

28

Citrus limon – lemon: the treatment for scurvy (at long last)

James Lind, in his book *On the scurvy* (1753), reported on his use of lemons to cure scurvy, but failed to recommend the fruit to the British admiralty. Consequently sailors continued to die horribly from vitamin C deficiency until lime juice was introduced to the British navy in 1795, following the second edition of Dr Gilbert Blane's *Observations on the diseases of seamen* (1789). However, physicians continued to believe Lind's hypothesis that scurvy was caused by the hot fetid air in the holds of ships in the tropics even though they accepted that citrus fruits were curative. Although the cure for scurvy, with the bark of *Drimys winteri*, had been known for 200 years, the delay in accepting a dietary cause and cure is amazing to us now. Woodville (1792) noted lemon's anti-scorbutic properties and discussed ways of processing lemon juice so it would keep on long voyages. Lindley (1838) makes no mention of it curing scurvy at all. Did he not believe it, or was scurvy so rare by then as to be no longer worthy of mention?

December

29

30

31

Notes

Euphorbia milii – Crown of thorns: an obscure doctor and forgotten anti-leukaemic drug

Euphorbus was the physician to the Berber King Juba II (50 BC-19 AD) of Numidia, a country that once existed within modern Tunisia and Algeria. Euphorbius' brother was Antonio Musa, after whom the genus Musa (the bananas) was named. Musa was physician to Octavius Augustus (63-14 BC), the first Roman Emperor. The plant is one of the tropical spurges with fierce cactus-like spines, widely grown as a house plant. Their highly irritant sap is used in folk medicine for treating warts (not very effective). Added to irrigation ditches it is a powerful molluscicide in the control of *Lymnaea columella*, the snail that is host to the parasitic trematode that causes fascioliasis. It also contains an anti-leukaemic chemical, lasiodiplodin, also found in a fungus called *Botrydiplodia theobromae*. Lasiodiplodin has not entered clinical use. King Juba II married Cleopatra Silene, the daughter of Mark Anthony and Cleopatra, and later the widow of the son of King Herod. He is commemorated in the name of the capital of South Sudan.

The Medicinal Garden of the Royal College of Physicians

The Royal College of Physicians' fifth home, at 11 St Andrews Place, was opened in 1965 with a small garden of medicinal plants. The present garden was initially designed and planted by Mark Griffiths in 2005 and by the head gardener, Jane Knowles, thereafter. The Socratic (poisons) garden was planted by the gardener, Clare Beacham.

In 2011 the garden contained 1,278 plants that have been used as medicines at some time in the past millennia up to the present day, from *Papaver somniferum* (morphine) to *Illicium anisatum* (Tamiflu); some selected because of the belief in the Doctrine of Signatures (*Pulmonaria officinalis*, *Hepatica nobilis*), others because of the humoural theory of the Greeks. There are plants whose poisons interfere with cell division (vincristine in *Catharanthus roseus*, taxol from *Taxus baccata*) so can be treatments for cancers, or are neurotoxins (atropine from *Atropa belladona*, scopolamine from *Scopolia carniolica*) useful for dilating the pupil and as a premedication before surgery.

In hundreds of ways the poisons/chemicals in plants have been harnessed by extraction, purification or modification for our health needs. Less than 40, out of the 400,000 species on the planet, have been licensed for sale in the UK as components of 'across the counter' herbal medications and none of them have to prove that they actually work.